This book belongs to ....
Age ....
Address ....
Telephone No. ....
Date ....

Greetings and best wishes to Snoopy's friends in the UK.

It is gratifying to know that the little black and white dog I draw so often is loved by people all over the world.

The "Peanuts" characters, especially Snoopy, have taken on lives of their own outside of the little boxes I put them in every day.

Folks sometimes tell me how often things happen to them to make them feel like Snoopy or Charlie Brown or Lucy or one of the others. Then I know I have created characters that people think of as friends.

I hope you'll continue to read "Peanuts" and to enjoy Snoopy and the gang.

Regards,

Charles M. Schulz

Snoopy
ANNUAL 1990

Based on the characters
created by
CHARLES M. SCHULZ

Written
by
Gordon Volke

RR
RAVETTE BOOKS

CONTENTS

Published by Ravette Books Limited 1989

Printed and bound for Ravette Books Limited,
3 Glenside Estate, Star Road,
Partridge Green, Horsham,
West Sussex RH13 8RA
Printed in Great Britain by
BPCC Paulton Books Limited

ISBN 1 85304 161 0

You're a Hero, Charlie Brown

"I've got the answer, Snoopy!" cried Charlie Brown. "Oh, good," thought Snoopy, who was dozing on top of his kennel, "but I didn't know there was a question!"

Charlie Brown stood up. "I've been reading my horoscope," he explained, "and it says 'if at first you don't succeed, try, try again.' That's all I need – practice!" Snoopy opened one eye and looked at his master. "What **is** the boy talking about?" he wondered.

Charlie Brown began pacing around, waving his arms about excitedly. "I want to be a hero," he exclaimed, "a sporting superstar. Then people will stop laughing at me and calling me 'blockhead'. Maybe even the Little Red-Haired Girl will fall in love with me."

Snoopy was still puzzled. "What's all this got to do with practice?" he thought to himself. Charlie Brown fetched his baseball bat. "I'm going to train all through the winter, "chuckled Charlie Brown, eagerly, "so when the new season starts, I'll be able to hit the ball every single time!" "I see!" thought Snoopy at last.

SWISH, SWIPE! SWIPE, SWISH! Charlie Brown's baseball bat flashed backwards and forwards as he tried to hit the ball. He missed every time. "I can't bear to watch," reflected Snoopy, closing his eyes.

Just then, Woodstock flew down to Snoopy's kennel. "Stop brushing my eyelids with your wings," called Snoopy, "it tickles." "!!!" replied Woodstock.

"What?" exclaimed Snoopy, sitting up suddenly and opening his eyes. "Hey, you're right! It's started to snow!"

The temperature went down and down. Soon, the water in Woodstock's bird-bath froze over. Snoopy fetched his ice-skates. "Yahoo!" chuckled Snoopy, "I can go ice-skating."

Woodstock watched his friend speeding around on his miniature ice-rink. "!!!!!" exclaimed the little bird, sadly. Snoopy skidded to a halt. "OOOPS!" cried the beagle, "I never thought of that!"

Woodstock was unhappy because the frozen bird-bath meant he had nowhere to wash or have a drink. Neither did Harriet, Conrad and all the rest of Woodstock's feathered friends. "Leave this to me," called Snoopy, taking off his skates and hat, "I'll smash the ice with my feeding-bowl."

BLAM, BLAM! Snoopy bashed the ice with his bowl. He did not succeed in breaking it – but he did manage to give himself toothache! "MMMFF!" groaned Snoopy.

Just then, Sally came along. She was all set to go skiing. "Don't worry, Snoopy," called Sally, seeing the problem, "I'll use one of my skis to break the ice." Snoopy and Woodstock watched excitedly as Charlie Brown's little sister thumped the ice with a ski. There was a loud, splintering noise – and the ski fell apart! "That's wonderful!" thought Snoopy, "Sally's skis have woodworm!"

Sally ran to Lucy's house and explained the problem "I know what to do!" cried Lucy, who had been listening to Shroeder practising his Beethoven, "We can use Shroeder's piano to crack the ice."

Lucy picked up the piano, but Shroeder snatched it back. "Hands off!" he snorted. "This instrument's priceless!"

Meanwhile, not far away, Charlie Brown was just coming out of his house in his winter coat."I'm not going to let a bit of snow stop me," he muttered, determinedly, "I'm going to keep on practising my baseball until I succeed."

SWISH, SWIPE! SWIPE, SWISH! The bat flashed backwards and forwards again, but **still** Charlie Brown did not make contact with the ball. "I'm going to try one last time," he puffed, "and if I miss, I'm going to give up the idea of being a star altogether!"

Charlie Brown tossed his baseball into the air and swung the bat at it. WHAP! He hit it! The ball soared up into the sky. "WOW!" gasped Charlie Brown, "I reckon it's gone into orbit!"

Back at the bird-bath, Woodstock was beginning to feel very thirsty and everyone was standing around, wondering how to break the ice. Suddenly, Charlie Brown's baseball descended from above and shattered the frozen surface into a million pieces! With a grateful chirp, Woodstock swooped down for a drink.

The children turned round and grinned."Nice work, Charlie Brown," called Lucy. As more and more of Woodstock's friends fluttered down to quench their thirst, everyone began to cheer Charlie Brown. They carried him round his house on their shoulders, singing 'For He's A Jolly Good Fellow'. Charlie Brown was thrilled. "I've turned out to be a hero after all!" he chuckled.

SPECIAL SNOOPY CROSSWORD

Across:

1. Snoopy lies on top of this. (8)
4. Initials of the Royal Air Force. (3)
7. This word can mean 'money' or 'to become different'. (6)
10. Snoopy and Woodstock always stand – – each other. (2)
12. They do a lot of this in Switzerland. (9)
15. 'Adios, goodbye, farewell, – – long. (2)
16. Opposite of 'was'. (2)
17. Snoopy leads these little soldiers on Nature-hikes. (6)
19. Two letters that mean 'morning-time'. (2)
20. One of Woodstock's friends – the girl who marries Bill. (7)
24. Same as 15 across. (2)
26. Spike sees a lot of these big, black birds in the desert. (7)
27. Light, sponge cake with a heavenly taste! (5)

Down:

1. A little white flower that grows on the grass (and the name of the Hill Farm where Snoopy was born). (5)
2. A game for the iced-up bird-bath. (6)
3. Delicious ice-creams, eaten on the day of rest. (7)
5. Snoopy, in his goggles, does a lot of this. (6)
6. A very special and famous breed of dog! (6)
8. Opposite of 'she'. (2)
11. One of these makes a tasty meal for Woodstock. (4)
13. Charlie Brown brings Snoopy his supper in this. (4)
14. Snoopy, the great author, is always writing one of these. (5)
15. This word means to have no food at all. (6)
18. Push aside – in the middle of 'glorious tennis'! (4)
19. As an alternative – take the 'me' out of 'more'. (2)
22. Snoopy, the pilot, is one of these. (3)
23. Wet weather for scout camp. (4)
25. The opposite of 'in'. (3)

Solution

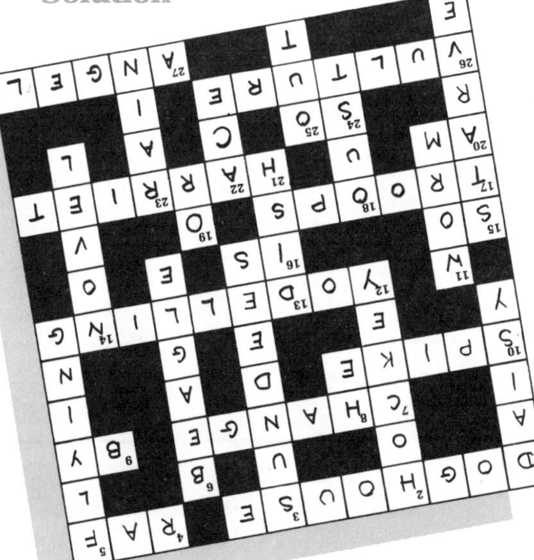

PEANUTS

featuring

"Good ol' Charlie Brown"

by SCHULZ

WHAT DO YOU HAVE THERE?

LAUNDRY DETERGENT
© 1985 United Feature Syndicate, Inc.

I DECIDED I HAVE TO LEARN TO DO SOME THINGS FOR MYSELF...

IT'S RIDICULOUS FOR A MAN NOT TO KNOW HOW TO DO HIS OWN LAUNDRY!
I AGREE

RATS!
WHAT'S THE PROBLEM?
4-14

HOW DO I GET THE SHIRT INTO THE BOTTLE?
SCHULZ

WHAT DO YOU THINK?

THIS IS A VALENTINE I BOUGHT FOR THAT LITTLE RED-HAIRED GIRL...

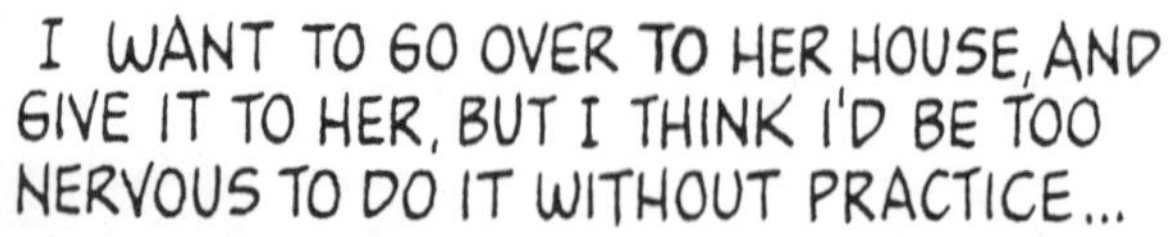

I WANT TO GO OVER TO HER HOUSE, AND GIVE IT TO HER, BUT I THINK I'D BE TOO NERVOUS TO DO IT WITHOUT PRACTICE...

I'LL GO OUTSIDE AND RING THE DOORBELL, AND YOU PRETEND YOU'RE THE LITTLE RED-HAIRED GIRL, OKAY?

2-10

RING!

SCHULZ

"Neither a borrower nor a lender be"
Shakespeare

"FOR LOAN OFT LOSES BOTH ITSELF AND FRIENDS"
WHAT?

LET ME BORROW YOUR RULER, MARCIE...
© 1984 United Feature Syndicate,Inc.

AS SOON AS YOU GIVE MY PEN BACK
IF I GIVE YOUR PEN BACK, I WON'T HAVE ANY USE FOR THE RULER..

SURE, YOU NEED MY PEN TO DRAW LINES WITH MY RULER ON THE TEN SHEETS OF PAPER YOU BORROWED FROM ME!

HERE, WHY DON'T YOU TAKE MY ERASER, MY NOTEBOOKS, MY COLORED PENCILS, MY COMB, MY LUNCH...

TAKE EVERYTHING I HAVE!!!

DO WE HAVE TIME FOR A GARAGE SALE, MA'AM?
SCHULZ
1-8

WE WISH YOU A

RY CHRISTMAS...

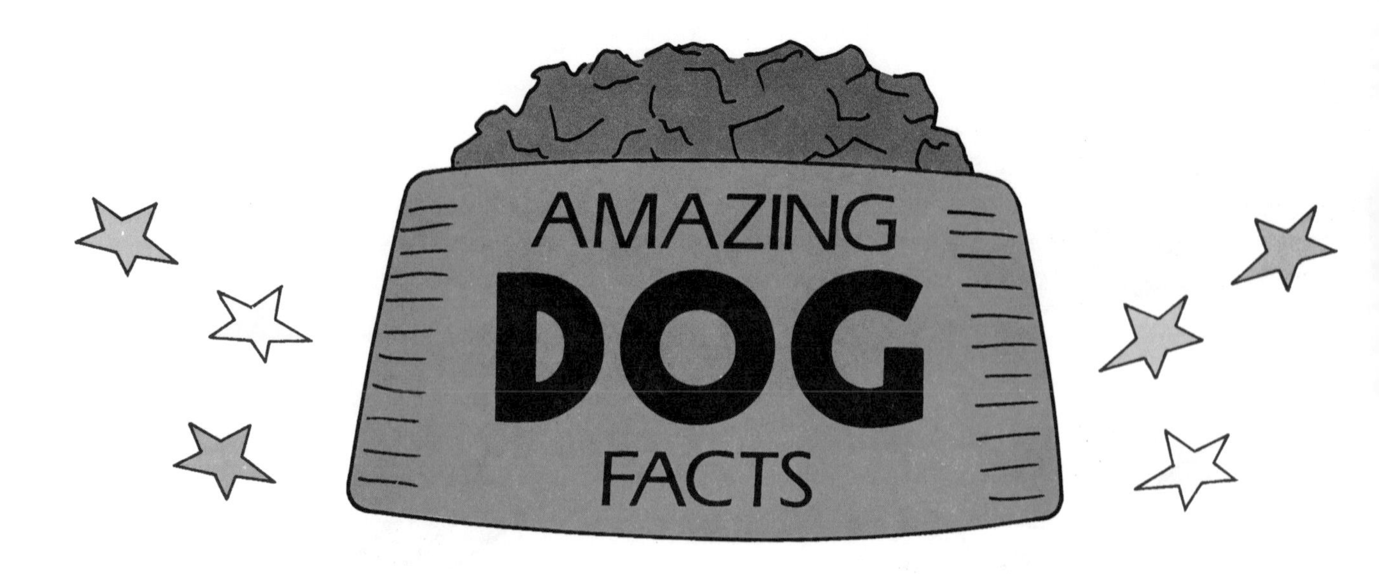

HEAVYWEIGHT CHAMP

We all know how much Snoopy enjoys the food brought to him by 'that round-headed kid', Charlie Brown. Snoopy has a lot of eating to do if he wants to catch up with the world's heaviest dog, an Old English mastiff called 'Alcama Zorba of La-Susa' owned by Chris Eraclides of London. Born in 1981, this amazing super-heavyweight tipped the scales at an incredible 144.66 kilograms (22 stone, 6½lb) in September 1987. Given that a man of average height weighs about 75 kilograms (roughly 12 stone), this means that 'Alcama' weighs almost as much as two fully-grown men!

MATCHBOX DOG

The smallest dog on record makes little Woodstock look like a giant American bald eagle! A miniature Yorkshire terrier, owned by Mr. Arthur F. Marples of Blackburn, Lancashire, was literally the size of a matchbox! When fully grown, this tiny dog only measured 9.5cm (3¾in) from the tip of his nose to the root of his tail and weighed an amazing 113g (4oz). The little terrier died in 1945 at the age of almost two years.

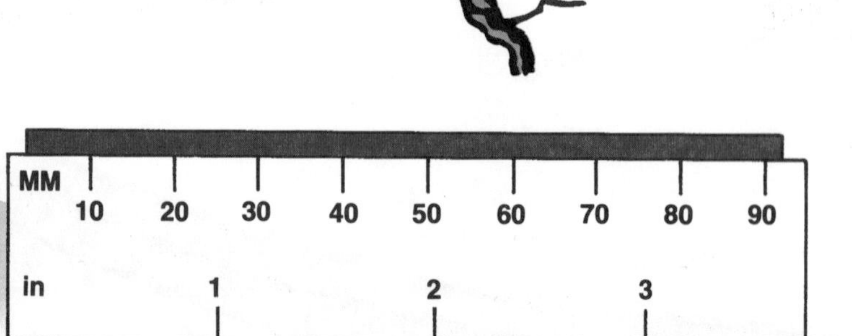

YOU CAN TEACH AN OLD DOG NEW TRICKS

The oldest dog in the world was an Australian cattle-dog named 'Bluey' who lived for an incredible 29 years and 5 months. Obtained as a puppy in 1910 by Mr. Les Hall of Victoria, Australia, Bluey worked among cattle and sheep for nearly 20 years. If you remember that most dogs live between 8 and 15 years and to live to 20 is very rare, to have been a WORKING dog for this length of time is truly astonishing.

Charlie Brown should take heart from this. He has been working on his football kick for many years now. Maybe, one day, he will get it right!

PUPPY POWER

The world record for the largest litter of puppies belongs to 'Lena', an American foxhound bitch owned by Commander W. N. Ely from Pennsylvania, USA. On June 19th, 1944, Lena gave birth to a total of 23 puppies and ALL of them survived!

The champion father of all time was a prize greyhound called 'Low Pressure' and nicknamed 'Timmy', owned by Mrs. Bruna Amhurst of Regent's Park, London. From December 1961 to his death on November 27th, 1969, Timmy fathered 2414 registered puppies as well as at least 600 unregistered ones!

(Lucy likes the sound of all these puppies. After all, she's heavily into 'puppy love', isn't she?)

Peppermint Patty and her faithful friend, Marcie, went to Summer Camp where one of the outdoor activities was tracking. They enjoyed following the signs and signals through the woods, but the game became a life-and-death struggle for a collie dog called 'Bobbie'. In 1923, Bobbie was lost by his owners while they were on holiday in Indiana, USA. Six months later, he turned up at the family home in Oregon, having covered a distance of 3,200 kilometers (around 2,000 miles)! The dog, later identified by householders who had looked after him along the route, had apparently travelled back through the states of Illinois, Iowa, Nebraska and Colorado, before crossing the Rocky Mountains in the depths of winter.

Information supplied and verified by The Guinness Book Of Records.

PEANUTS®
featuring
"Good ol' Charlie Brown"
by SCHULZ

WOODSTOCK! OLIVIER! CONRAD! WILSON!

OKAY, DO YOU ALL KNOW WHY WE'RE HERE?
? ? ? ?

THIS IS GOING TO BE WHAT WE CALL A NATURE HIKE

WELL, YES, IT DOES LOOK LIKE IT MIGHT SNOW...

SO YOU'D BETTER BRING YOUR MITTENS, OKAY?

12-2
© 1984 United Feature Syndicate,Inc.

SCHULZ

WHEN YOU LIVE ALONE IN THE DESERT, YOU HAVE TO MAKE UP YOUR OWN GAMES

I'LL BE THE QUARTERBACK AND YOU'LL BE THE RECEIVER..

HERE WE GO!

2-19
© 1984 United Feature Syndicate, Inc.

WOW! WHAT A CATCH!!
PLUNK!

SSSSSSS

OF COURSE, SOME GAMES ARE BETTER THAN OTHERS..

YOU'RE KIDDING
NO, I'M SERIOUS

YOU DON'T CARE ANYTHING ABOUT ANYBODY...

YOU NEVER SHOW ANY INTEREST IN WHAT ANYONE ELSE IS DOING..YOU NEVER ASK QUESTIONS...

YOU NEVER ASK ME WHAT I'M READING, HOW I'M DOING IN SCHOOL, WHERE I GOT MY NEW SHOES...

YOU NEVER ASK ME WHAT I THINK ABOUT SOMETHING, OR WHAT I BELIEVE, OR WHAT I KNOW, OR WHERE I'M GOING, OR WHERE I'VE BEEN OR ANYTHING!
5-19

IF YOU'RE GOING TO SHOW INTEREST IN OTHER PEOPLE, YOU HAVE TO ASK QUESTIONS...

HOW HAVE YOU BEEN?
SCHULZ

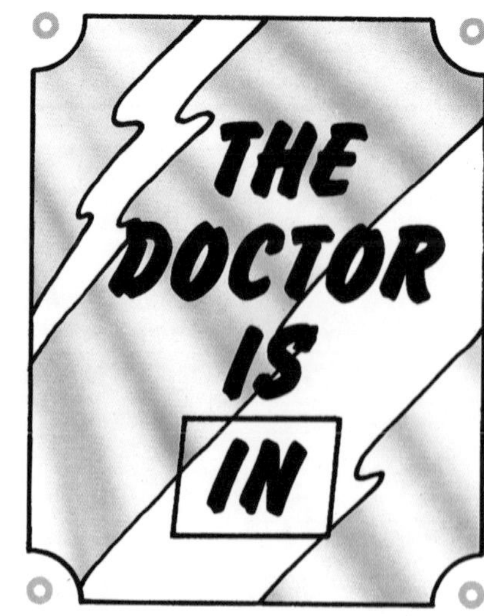

Do you have a problem? Something that's worrying you? If so, Dr. Lucy Van Pelt is at your service!

These two pages contain a selection of letters from her enormous postbag. Dr. Lucy answers each question with words of advice that draw upon years of experience counselling Charlie Brown and giving instruction to her friends.

Remember this modest motto:
'When in doubt – ask Lucy!"

Problem: I get very upset about people talking behind my back. What should I do about it?
Lucy answers: Give up being a taxi-driver.

Problem: I feel a terrible failure. I am a scout, but I am no good at lighting fires out of doors. What can I do?
Lucy answers: Try lighting fires out of sticks. Doors don't burn very well.

Problem: I am very poor at counting. Do you think I should buy a pocket calculator?
Lucy answers: Do you need to know how many pockets you've got?

Problem: I think my house is haunted. Someone keeps knocking on my door, but when I answer it there's nobody there. What should I do about this invisible caller?
Lucy answers: Tell him you can't see him.

Problem: Please can you help me. I suffer from terrible insomnia. Night after night I cannot go to sleep. What can I do?
Lucy answers: Lie on the edge of the bed. You'll soon drop off.

Problem: My little boy keeps playing with the telephone. The other day dialled 666. What do you think will happen?
Lucy answers: The Police will arrive upside-down.

Problem: I desperately want to be a puppeteer when I grow up, but I've heard it's hard to break into show business. How would you advise me to start my career?
Lucy answers: Get someone to pull a few strings for you.

Problem: I have thinning hair and have recently bought a wig. Do you think I should tell my friends that my hair is false?
Lucy answers: I should just keep it under your hat.

Problem: I have a very embarrassing problem. Every lunch time, a boy I don't fancy comes and sits on my right hand and tries to chat me up. How can I get rid of him?
Lucy answers: Tell him to sit on a chair like everyone else.

Problem: I am very worried about my husband. He thinks he's a TV aerial. Last night, he spent the entire evening sitting on top of the set. What can I do with him?
Lucy answers: Try turning him round. You might get a better picture on BBC 2.

Problem: I met a man in the bus the other day. He strongly advised me to sleep with my window open. Do you think he was a doctor?
Lucy answers: No, a burglar.

Problem: My life is being made a misery by a squirrel. He keeps coming into the house and stealing food. How can I make the pest go away?
Lucy answers: Climb up his tree and act like a nut.

A final word from the doctor – if you take this advice seriously, you have a **real** problem!

S
S
S
S

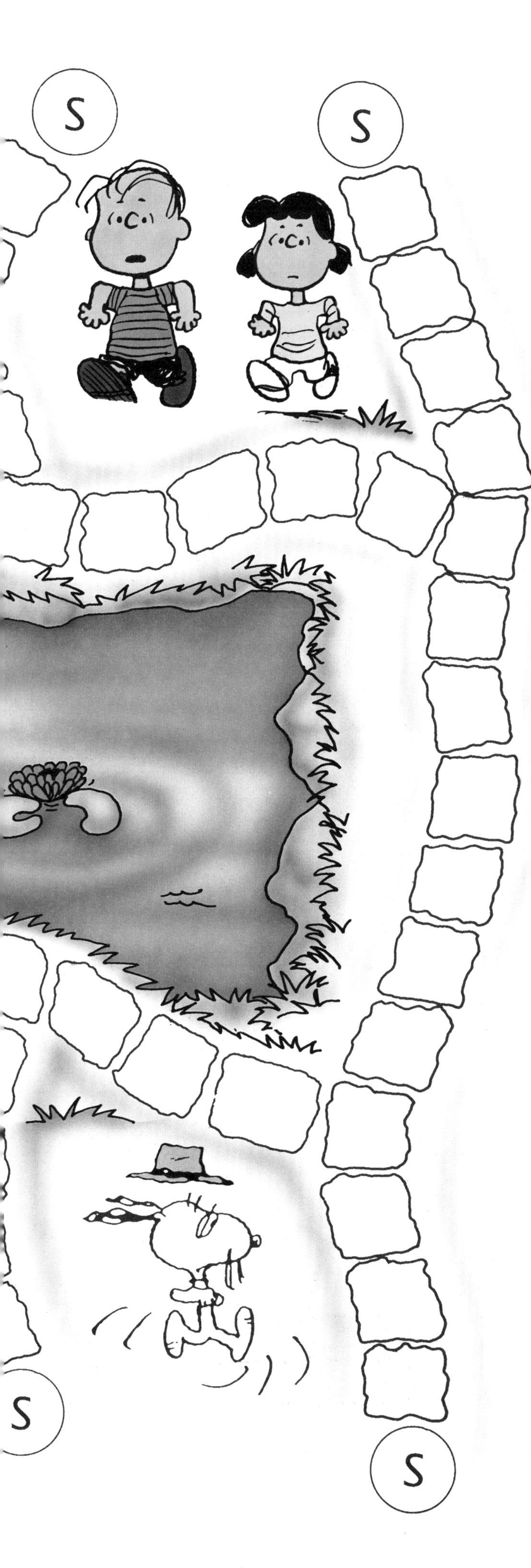

Snoopy's Fun-Run

Snoopy, the fitness-freak, decided to go for a jog. Charlie Brown, Linus and Lucy went with him. "We can run round the lake," thought Snoopy. On the way, they met Spike, Sally, Peppermint Patty and Marcie, coming in the opposite direction. They were jogging too. "We challenge you to a race!" called Charlie Brown. "You're on!" replied the others. So the fun-run began!

You can join in too. All you need is a die and eight counters. These can come from another game or you can use buttons. Four counters must be one colour and four another. The game is easy to play and needs two players or two teams.

These are the rules. Four paths of the same length lead to the lake from the top and four from the bottom. Snoopy's team are one colour (say red) and Spike's team another (say blue). The four red counters are placed in the spaces marked 'S' above the lake and the four blue ones in the corresponding spaces below. Each player must throw a six to start. Once this is done, he moves his counters down the track towards the lake. Each 'runner' has to go right round the lake and finish up at the opposite starting-point.

If two opponents land on the same square together, the one who got there first can send the other away. This second 'runner' must return to the beginning and start all over again! The winner is the person whose counters reach the opposite side of the lake first.

NOTE:
It doesn't matter which way round the lake the 'runners' go – but jumping or swimming across is definitely NOT allowed!

PEANUTS®
featuring
"Good ol' Charlie Brown"
by SCHULZ

GOOD EVENING, SIR..WOULD YOU LIKE TO SEE A MENU?

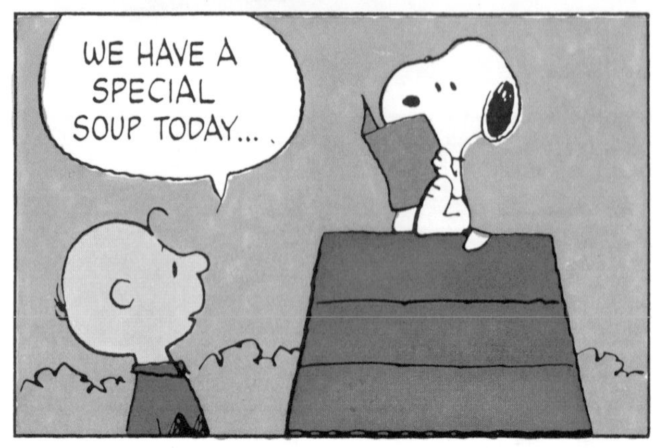
WE HAVE A SPECIAL SOUP TODAY...

"CREAM OF DOG FOOD"!
4-1
© 1984 United Feature Syndicate, Inc.

HA HA HA HA HA HA!

BONK!

FUNNY WAITERS NEED TO BE STRUCK WITH A MENU AT LEAST ONCE A WEEK!
SCHULZ

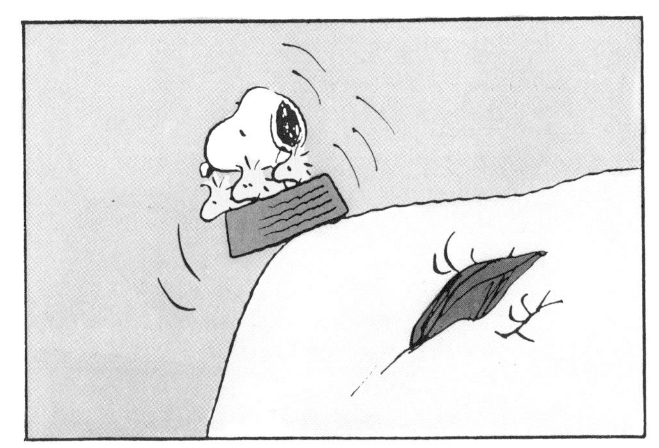

TRAINING AND DISCIPLINE.. THAT'S THE SECRET...

DON'T FORGET THE COMMAND

I'LL GIVE THE ORDER..

BE READY..

BONK!

ABANDON SUPPER DISH!!

2-26
SEE? TRAINING AND DISCIPLINE!
SCHULZ

Z

Z

2-17
Z

YES, MA'AM, I'M READY...

© 1985 United Feature Syndicate, Inc.
Z

THIS IS MY REPORT ON THE HUMAN HEAD.. I WON'T BORE YOU BY READING ALL OF THE DETAILS...
Z

HOWEVER, INSIDE MY LOOSE-LEAF BINDER IS A FULL-SCALE MODEL OF THE HUMAN HEAD...

THANK YOU, MA'AM.. I'M GLAD YOU LIKED MY REPORT
I'LL GET YOU FOR THIS, MARCIE.. AS SOON AS I FIND OUT WHAT'S GOING ON, I'LL GET YOU FOR THIS...
SCHULZ

RATS!

I CAN'T STAND IT!

STUPID KNOTS! SHOELACES DRIVE ME CRAZY!!

GRAMPA TOLD ME SOMETHING ABOUT SHOELACES AND WORLD WAR II
© 1985 United Feature Syndicate, Inc.
3-3

HE SAID ALL THE ENLISTED MEN WERE ISSUED TWO PAIRS OF SHOES, BUT A LOT OF THE MEN WORE ONLY ONE PAIR SO THEY COULD KEEP THE OTHER PAIR SHINED AND LOOKING NICE UNDER THEIR BUNKS...

BATTALION HEADQUARTERS DECIDED THAT THE MEN SHOULD ALTERNATE SHOES EACH DAY, AND TO MAKE SURE THEY DID, THE MEN HAD TO LACE THEIR SHOES IN A CERTAIN WAY...

ONE DAY THEY HAD TO WEAR THE SHOES WHICH HAD THE LACES CROSSED, AND THE NEXT DAY THEY HAD TO WEAR THE SHOES WHICH HAD THE LACES GOING STRAIGHT ACROSS...

HOW DID THEY EVER WIN THE WAR?
SCHULZ

Rerun, Lucy and Linus's baby brother, has written a story specially for the youngest Snoopy fans (and everyone else who is young at heart). Some of the words have been replaced by pictures which makes the story extra fun to read.

WAS LYING ON HIS
IN THE BRIGHT, SUMMER SUNSHINE. "PHEW!" HE GASPED,
"I'M A VERY
!" SO HE CALLED TO
WHO WAS BUSY CHASING A
.
"COME ON,
," EXCLAIMED
, "LET'S GO 2 THE
."
AND
WENT
ON THE
. AS SOON AS THEY REACHED THE
, THEY RAN DOWN TO THE
. "I'M GOING 4 A SWIM!" ANNOUNCED
. "BE CAREFUL!" WARNED
,
"THERE'S A BIG
OVER THERE AND THEY
STING!"
AFTER HIS REFRESHING DIP,
FELT HUNGRY. "TIME 2 EAT!" HE SAID TO
.
SO THEY TUCKED INTO SOME TASTY
THEY HAD BROUGHT WITH THEM,
FOLLOWED BY A DELICIOUS
FROM THE
CAFE.
"NOW WE JUST HAVE TIME FOR A GAME OF
," SAID
, "AND A QUICK RIDE ON THE
."
SOON IT WAS TIME TO CATCH THE
AGAIN.
AND
WERE
TIRED AFTER THEIR EXCITING DAY OUT.
"ISN'T IT NICE TO BE
," SMILED
.

COLOURING PICTURE

Here is a picture of the entire Peanuts Gang. You can colour the picture with felt-tips, paints or crayons.

40 YEARS OF SNOOPY

"It seems beyond the comprehension of people that someone can be born to draw comic strips, but I think I was."

Charles Schulz

1990 marks the 40th anniversary of the Peanuts comic strip. Since it first appeared in a handful of American newspapers on October 2nd, 1950, Charles M. Schulz has lovingly drawn every figure and penned every word in more than 14,000 strips. In doing so, he has created the most popular comic strip in the history of publishing.

Peanuts is the most widely-read comic strip in the world, appearing in more than 2,200 newspapers in 68 countries and 26 languages. Snoopy and the Gang are known and loved throughout the United States, Europe, South America, the Middle East and Asia. As a result of this enormous popularity, it is believed that the figure of Snoopy is known and recognised by more people than any other imaginary character in world literature!

The enduring appeal of Snoopy and his friends has led to more than 1,000 books, 30 television specials and four feature films. Paperback collections of the picture strip have sold more than 300 million copies to date. The 30 prime-time TV specials, originally shown on the CBS network in America, have gained 24 Emmy nominations and won six. Many of the TV specials and the four feature films have been shown worldwide.

Peanuts has also given birth to two musicals. The first was called 'You're A Good Man, Charlie Brown'. It proved to be a long-running Broadway success and remains one of the most widely produced musicals in America today. The second show, which was also very popular, was just called 'Snoopy!'

Snoopy and company have been delighting readers for generations and it is no surprise that Schulz has been honoured for his work. Two of the TV specials won Peabody Awards which recognise 'distinguished and meritorious public service'. Also, he has been given two highly prestigious Reuben Awards by the National Cartoonists Society.

Charles M. Schulz is the man who has given the world '40 Years Of Happiness'.

UP, UP AND AWAY

Snoopy has lost Woodstock! The beagle's tiny companion went up in his balloon and was blown away by the strong wind. To reach Woodstock, Snoopy must make his ears spin round and take off into the sky. Can you help Snoopy to find his way through the clouds?

Snoopy often lies on top of his kennel, dreaming about chocolate chip cookies. If you share his passion for these delicious biscuits, here's how to make them yourself.

Ingredients
100g (4oz) butter
100g (4oz) caster sugar
2 tbsp condensed milk
75g (3oz) plain chocolate chips
175g (6oz) self-raising flour

Method
Heat the oven to 150°C (300F). Cream the butter and sugar together until light and fluffy, then beat in the condensed milk. Sprinkle in the chocolate chips. (These can be bought in a packet at the shops. They are better than chopping a bar of chocolate into chips because they are the right size and they don't melt so easily.) Sift the flour and work into the mixture. Mix the dough well, then roll into walnut-sized balls.
Place on greased tinfoil and press down with a fork. Bake for 25-30 minutes or until golden brown. Cool on a wire rack.

Quick tip:
Cookies are more difficult to remove from the baking sheet after they've cooled completely. If you have any trouble getting them off, just pop them back into a warm oven for a few minutes.

Final word of warning – keep the cookies away from your dog!

Sally's Christmas Party

"Where IS everyone?" asked Sally, looking out of the window. It was the afternoon of her Christmas Party. All the food was ready and the orange juice was chilling in the fridge. So far, however, only Linus had turned up.

"What do you think has happened, Sweet Babboo?" sighed Sally. "I'm not your Sweet Babboo!" replied Linus, "Did you send out the invitations?" "Of course I did!" retorted Sally, "You received yours, didn't you?" Then Sally stopped. "Oh, dear!" she exclaimed, "Oh, dear-oh-dear!"

Sally hurried to her coat pocket. There were the rest of the party invitations! "I posted yours first," she explained to Linus, "and I began daydreaming about the fun we'd have together at the party. I must have forgotton to post the others." "Oh, dear-oh-dear!" agreed Linus. Sally hurried to the telephone, but there was no reply from the rest of their friends. They were all out playing. "What are we going to do?" sighed Sally.

Suddenly, Linus remembered seeing a packet of balloons. "If we hang balloons on the front door," he cried, excitedly, "everyone will know that's the signal for a party!"

PUFF! PUFF! Sally and Linus were feeling light-headed by the time they had blown up the balloons. Linus tied on the strings and carried a bunch towards the front door. "Mind the holly. . ." warned Sally. It was too late. BANG! BANG! BANG! Linus was left holding the empty strings. "Allow me to help you!" said Sally, marching to the door with the rest of the balloons. She opened the door and . . . WHOOSH. The other balloons blew away! "What are we going to do **now?**" groaned Sally.

Just then, Snoopy came in with Charlie Brown. Sally explained the problem. "Semaphore!" thought Snoopy, "That's the answer!" The brainy beagle scampered off to find his collection of signalling-flags. Then he clambered onto the top of his kennel and began to wave them backwards and forwards. "Now all we have to do is wait," thought Snoopy.

Everyone waited and waited – but nobody turned up for the party. "Nice try, Snoopy," said Charlie Brown, "but nobody understands semaphore except you!"

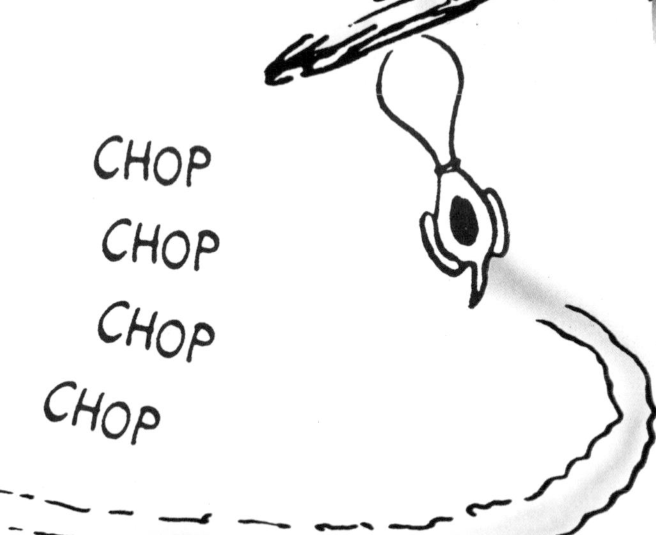

Snoopy was not to be beaten. He remained on top of his kennel and began revolving his ears. "I'll fly round and point everyone in the direction of the party," he thought to himself.

CHOP! CHOP! CHOP! Snoopy took off into the air, but he did not know where to find the rest of their friends. He flew round and round in circles until his ears grew tired. "OOOER!" thought Snoopy, "I appear to be losing height."

BLAM! Snoopy plummeted downwards and crash-landed onto the ground. He sat up, feeling dazed and shaken. "Huh!" thought Snoopy, "Me and my big ideas!"

Charlie Brown stepped forward. "Leave this to me," he proclaimed, "I'll solve the problem with my trusty kite." Charlie Brown fetched a felt-tip pen and wrote 'COME TO THE PARTY' on one side of the material. "Now I'll fly this high in the sky," he chuckled, "and everyone will see the message."

Everybody knows the trouble Charlie Brown has flying his kite! This particular afternoon was no exception. He ran up and down outside the house, trying to get the kite into the air. It just kept bumping back onto the ground! Then a stronger gust of wind lifted it skywards – but Snoopy became tangled in the kite-string. Beagle and kite came spiralling back to earth. "Sorry, old fella," said Charlie Brown, "I guess it isn't your day – or mine!"

Snoopy sat rubbing his head. The action caused another brilliant idea to pop into his nimble brain. With an excited bark, Snoopy fetched Linus's blanket. Then he picked up Charlie Brown's pen and began to write the word 'PARTY' on the blanket. "I get it!" exclaimed Sally, "We fly the blanket like a flag."

Everyone loved Snoopy's idea – except Linus! "Nobody touches my precious blanket," he yelled, "let go of it, you daft dog!"

In the end, there seemed no way to let everyone know about the Christmas Party. Sally became very upset. "It's all my fault!" sobbed Charlie Brown's little sister, "Christmas is ruined because of me!" Sally took herself off to bed.

Gloom descended on the household. Charlie Brown, Linus and Snoopy tried to eat the party food, but it stuck in their throats. "Anyone fancy a drink?" asked Linus. "No, thanks," sighed Charlie Brown, miserably. Then there was a knock on the door. Charlie Brown shuffled to open it. Lucy, Shroeder and all the rest of their friends were standing on the doorstep. "We've come to the party!" beamed Lucy.

Sally came hurrying down the stairs. "I don't understand!" she cried, "How did you know about the party?" "The balloons," smiled Shroeder, pointing out of the door. The balloons that blew away from Sally had caught round a tree beside the front gate. "We all came running as soon as we saw the signal!" laughed Lucy.

Soon, the Christmas Party was in full swing. Sally enjoyed it most of all. "Isn't it fun, my Sweet Babboo?" she whooped. "Yes," agreed Linus, "but I'm NOT your Sweet Babboo!"

SPOT THE DIFFERENCE

There are 10 differences between these two pictures of Snoopy and Charlie Brown in the school canteen. Some are easy to find; others are a bit more tricky. Can you spot them all? The answers are printed upside down at the bottom of this page.

Answers

1. Peppermint Patty has lost the freckles from one side of her face.
2. The tray on the top of the pile has lost its indentation.
3. Half of the spaghetti is missing from the serving dish.
4. Three of the plates behind Charlie Brown have disappeared.
5. Charlie Brown has lostthe zig zag pattern from his sweater.
6. Sally has lost the words 'PEANUTS UNIVERSITY,' from her apron.
7. The sandwich in her serving-tongs has disappeared.
8. Two toes are missing from Snoopy's left foot.
9. The pattern has disappeared from the sole of Linus's shoe.
10. Linus has no sandwiches on his plate.

NOT JUST FOR CHRISTMAS

Everyone is familiar with the slogan, 'A dog is for life, not just for Christmas.' Yet the sad fact is that, every year, an increasing number of puppies which are bought as Christmas presents end up on the streets because their owners have discovered they're more than just a pair of melting, brown eyes and big, funny feet. So, if you are thinking of getting a pet this Christmas, here are some basic DOs and DON'Ts of looking after a puppy.

Do Choose Your Puppy Carefully

It is important to know what kind of dog you want. There are hundreds of different breeds and they all have their own special characteristics. You may like the look of an Old English Sheepdog, but will you have time to groom it? You may think it's fun to throw a stick for a Golden Retriever, but will you want to turn out on a rainy day in the middle of winter? It is best to work out in advance what type of demands will be made upon you by the dog you choose. More dog/owner relationships fail through choosing the wrong type of animal than for any other reason.

Do Give Your Puppy Plenty Of Exercise

Unless you have a very small dog or a very large garden, you will need to take your pet for frequent walks. The youngest puppies need less exercise and time to sleep without being disturbed, but it won't be long before your little dog is bursting for his daily run. If he does not get enough exercise, he will become fat and this can lead to health problems in later life. Equally important, he will become bored and you will probably return from the shops to find the sofa has been chewed to pieces!

Do Train Your Puppy

Training in obedience is essential to every dog. Your puppy should be taught to come when called; to walk on a lead without pulling or being pulled, and to sit or lie down when told. It is not cruel to 'master' your dog. In fact, the opposite is true. An obedient dog is a happy dog because he knows exactly what is expected of him.

Don't Have A Puppy At All Unless:

1. You can afford to keep it. Dog food and vet bills are expensive.
2. You have time for your puppy. Dogs need constant companionship and exercise.
3. You have room for your puppy. Are your house and garden suitable for a young dog? Can he escape?

Don't Feed 'On Demand'

Puppies should be fed at the same time every day. An 8-week-old puppy should have 4 small meals a day, spread out between early morning, lunch time, late afternoon and evening. If your puppy is not fed at regular intervals, he will always be under your feet, scrounging for food. Remember, also, that your dog should always have plenty of fresh drinking water available.

Don't Forget To Say 'Good Dog'

Dogs LOVE praise. They learn much more quickly if you praise them for doing something right rather than scolding them for doing something wrong. Dog-training should be given every day by the same person. It should only be for a short period and your puppy should always be treated with kindness, patience and control. Whatever happens, your motto must be 'LOVE YOUR DOG'. Unlike cats, who tend to be self-centred and independent, dogs are complex emotional creatures who want nothing more than to please you. That's why, – whether high-born pedigree or lowly mongrel – they are such endearing and faithful companions.

**Information kindly provided by the RSPCA.
For detailed booklet, 'Dogs and Puppies', write to: RSPCA, The Causeway, Horsham, West Sussex RH12 1HG.**

PEANUTS
featuring
"Good ol' Charlie Brown"
by SCHULZ

SIGH

THERE'S THE TELEPHONE..I'D GIVE ANYTHING TO HAVE THE NERVE TO CALL THAT LITTLE RED HAIRED GIRL...
WHY DON'T YOU JUST DO IT?
BECAUSE I KNOW SHE WOULDN'T WANT TO TALK TO ME...

THAT'S RIDICULOUS, CHARLIE BROWN.. WE SEE HER IN SCHOOL EVERY DAY... SHE'S A VERY NICE PERSON!
SHE'LL TALK TO YOU..I KNOW SHE WILL...
I DOUBT IT..I'D JUST BE MAKING A FOOL OF MYSELF
12-1

GO AHEAD.. DO IT! CALL HER!
ALL RIGHT, BUT I'LL BET SHE WON'T EVEN GIVE ME THE TIME OF DAY...

WELL, WHAT HAPPENED?
SHE SAID IT WAS FOUR O'CLOCK!
SCHULZ

HE'S GONNA BE SURPRISED

ATTENTION, TROOPS!
4-22

THIS IS A HISTORIC OCCASION..
© 1984 United Feature Syndicate, Inc.

ONE OF OUR MEMBERS HAS COMPLETED ALL OF HIS TESTS, AND IS NOW ELIGIBLE TO RECEIVE THE "BEAGLE SCOUT" AWARD!

CONRAD, PLEASE STEP FORWARD..

IT GIVES ME GREAT PLEASURE TO PIN THIS BEAUTIFUL BRONZE "BEAGLE SCOUT" AWARD TO THE SIDE OF YOUR HAT...

KLUNK!
SCHULZ

MADAM ABSOLUTELY, THERE IS NO DOUBT, FULLCHARGE

GET UP!

YOU'RE LYING IN MY BEANBAG
IT'S NOT YOUR BEANBAG, AND I WAS HERE FIRST...

LET'S MAKE AN AGREEMENT..
A WHAT?
1-15

YOU CAN HAVE IT SOME OF THE TIME...

..AND I'LL HAVE IT MOST OF THE TIME!

BIG SISTERS ARE ALL OF THE TIME!
SCHULZ

AH! CLEAR AND SUNNY!

ATTENTION, EVERYBODY!

WELCOME TO THE CACTUS CLUB SPORTS DAY!

OUR FIRST RACE WILL BE TWENTY LAPS...

THAT MEANS DOWN AND BACK, DOWN AND BACK, TEN TIMES...

JUST REMEMBER, WE'RE OUT HERE TO HAVE FUN...

ARE THERE ANY QUESTIONS?

YES, WELL, BECAUSE THIS IS A SWIM RACE, I GUESS WE DO HAVE ONE SMALL PROBLEM...

...AND A H

y NEW YEAR

SNOOPY SPORTS QUIZ

This easy fun-quiz will help you to discover the enormous range of Snoopy's sporting talent! Below are 10 pictures of the super-fit beagle taking part in different sports. Do you know their names? To help you, we have printed the names with all the letters jumbled up. All you have to do is to sort them out and write them correctly in the spaces underneath. The answers are printed upside down at the end of the quiz.

ABSTABLKEL

KGIHIN

ACRMIEAN-OOTAFBLL

AREWT-ISIKNG

SEALBLABB

ECI - CKHYOE

Answers

Tennis	Fishing	Wind-surfing	Golf	Basketball
Hiking	American-football	Water-skiing	Baseball	Ice-hockey

PEANUTS®
featuring
"Good ol' Charlie Brown"
by SCHULZ

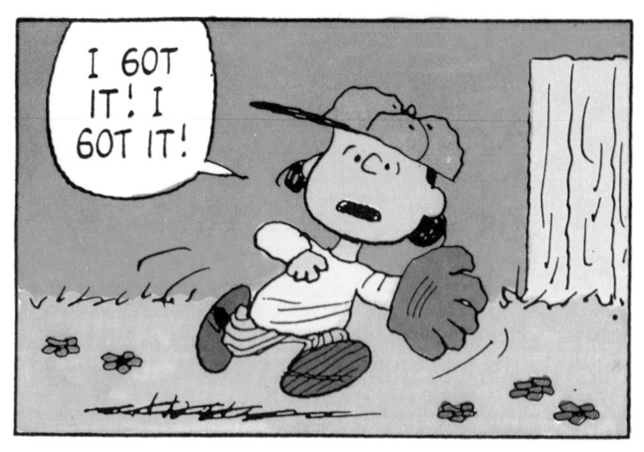

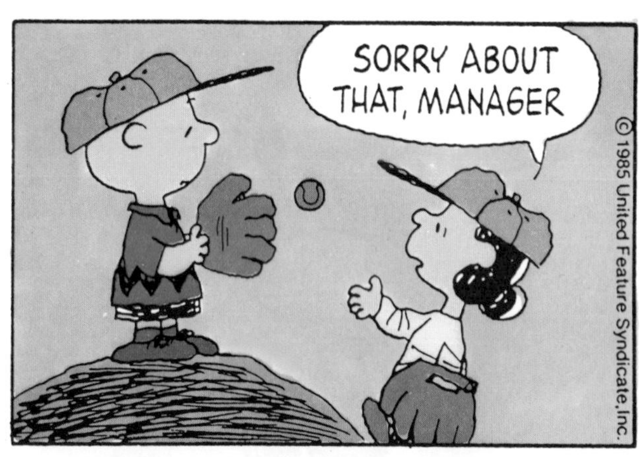

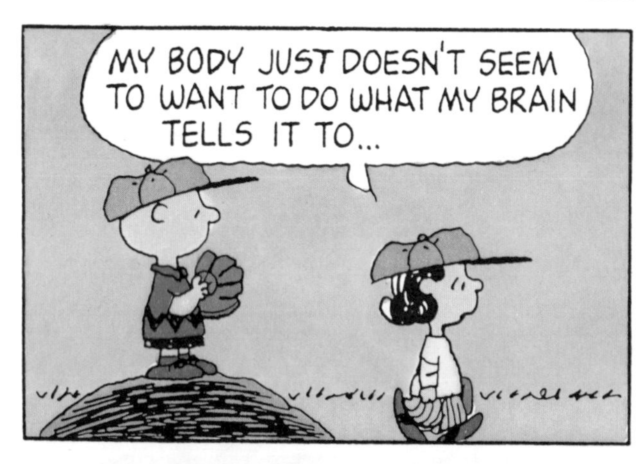

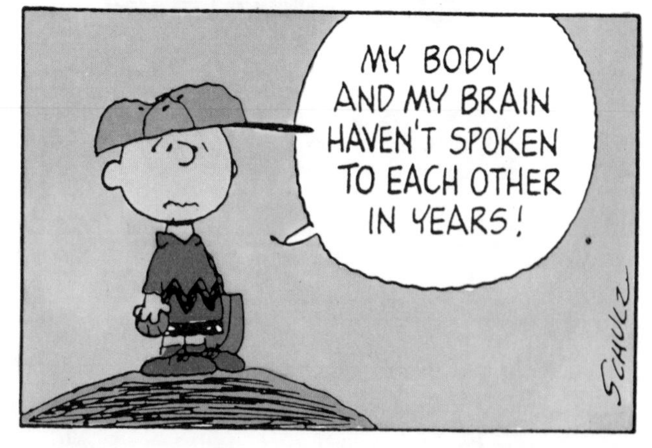

NO, MA'AM

NOW I FEEL GUILTY!

I'M SO ASHAMED OF MYSELF
© 1985 United Feature Syndicate,Inc.
3-24

I TOLD THE TEACHER I DIDN'T HAVE MY HOMEWORK DONE BECAUSE I WASN'T FEELING WELL LAST NIGHT..

ACTUALLY, I WAS WATCHING TV...NOW, I'LL BE PUNISHED WITH BAD LUCK... OR SOMEBODY IN OUR FAMILY WILL HAVE BAD LUCK...

YOU'RE JUST SUPERSTITIOUS

NO ONE COULD REALLY BELIEVE THAT SOMEBODY IN YOUR FAMILY WOULD HAVE BAD LUCK BECAUSE OF SOMETHING YOU DID...

BONK

HAS MY SISTER BEEN LYING AGAIN?!
SCHULZ

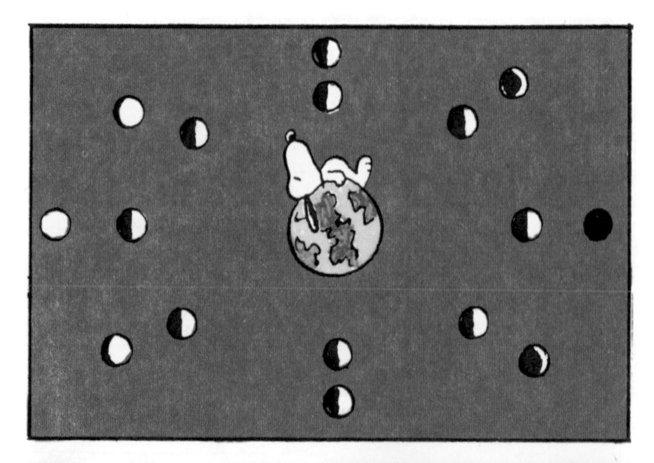

LOOK, THERE'S A FULL MOON TONIGHT

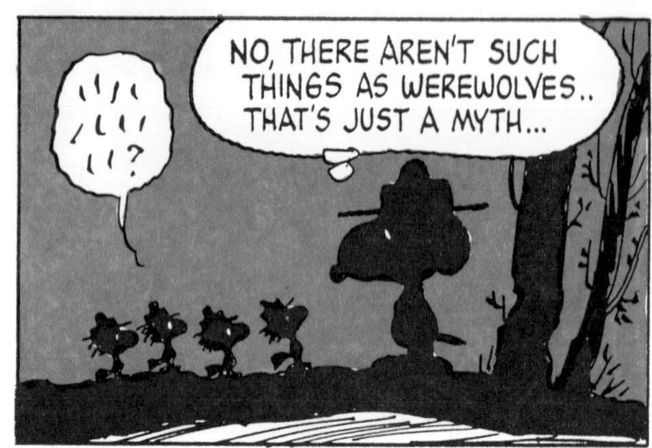
NO, THERE AREN'T SUCH THINGS AS WEREWOLVES.. THAT'S JUST A MYTH...

BUT I'LL LET YOU IN ON A LITTLE SECRET..

10-21
YOU KNOW WHO REALLY COMES OUT WHEN THE MOON IS FULL?
© 1984 United Feature Syndicate, Inc.

WEREBEAGLE!!

WHY DO I DO THINGS LIKE THAT?

YES, MA'AM, I WALKED TO SCHOOL IN THE RAIN..I HAD TO PUT MY BINDER ON MY HEAD TO KEEP FROM GETTING SOAKED...
5-6

MY REPORT? WELL, IT'S INSIDE THE BINDER, AND I THINK THE BINDER HAS RUSTED TO MY HEAD...
© 1984 United Feature Syndicate, Inc.

I'LL JUST SORT OF REST THE WHOLE BUSINESS ON YOUR DESK, AND MAYBE YOU CAN PEEK IN THROUGH THE EDGES...

YOU'D BETTER HURRY, MA'AM.. I THINK I'M SLIPPING...

KLUNK!

THAT'S CUTE, MA'AM..YOU SOUND LIKE A LITTLE PUPPY WHEN YOU WHIMPER LIKE THAT..
SCHULZ

WHAT'S THIS?

CAN'T YOU TELL?

PSYCHIATRIC HELP 5¢
THIS IS THE FAMOUS PSYCHIATRIC "CAKE" TEST...
THE DOCTOR IS IN

WE CAN TELL A LOT ABOUT A PATIENT BY OBSERVING WHICH HE EATS FIRST, THE CAKE OR THE FROSTING...
THE DOCTOR IS IN

CHOCOLATE IS ACTUALLY MY FAVORITE..

!?

NOW FROM THIS LITTLE EXPERIMENT, DO YOU THINK WE CAN TELL WHAT YOU NEED IN YOUR LIFE?

ANOTHER PIECE OF CAKE AND A CLEAN PLATE!
SCHULZ
3-25

SCUBA-DIVING SNOOPY

It was the middle of the summer holidays. Snoopy lay outside in the warm sunshine, reading a magazine. The article was all about deep-sea diving. "I'd love to do that," sighed Snoopy, closing his eyes and imagining himself swimming down towards a sunken galleon, "wrecks on the sea-bed and all that stuff is so romantic!"

Woodstock overheard his best friend's wish. "!!!!!" he called. "Really?" exclaimed Snoopy, "You have a pirate ship that I can sail on?" Then Snoopy saw where the galleon was. "Er, perhaps not, old chap," he smiled.

So Snoopy and Woodstock sat on top of Snoopy's kennel. "Let's **pretend** to be deep-sea divers!" chuckled Snoopy. The chums imagined that the kennel was a boat. "Prepare to dive overboard." announced Snoopy, in a deep commander's voice. Unfortunately, the two of them grew carried away by their game. They launched themselves overboard and KLUNK! KLUNK! Snoopy and Woodstock hit the ground! "!!!!!" squawked Woodstock. "I agree," groaned Snoopy, "you need water to go deep-sea diving!"

Later that day, Snoopy set off for the beach with Charlie Brown, Sally, Lucy and Linus. Woodstock did not go. He still had a slight headache and stayed in his nest.

Snoopy led the way. He loved going to the beach with his friends."I wonder what everyone's going to do?" he thought to himself.

Linus made straight for the golden sand and began to dig. Snoopy thought it was the funniest-looking sandcastle he had ever seen. "I'm making a sand-model of The Great Pumpkin," explained Linus. The idea needed a great deal of sand, so Snoopy helped by digging with his paws. It was hot work. "I'm going to leave Linus to it," thought Snoopy.

The beagle went to see where Lucy was. Lucy was being far more sensible on such a hot day, sitting in her beach-chair and rubbing in sun-tan oil. As Snoopy approached, Lucy held out the bottle to him. "Very kind," thought Snoopy, "but you don't get sunburned when you're covered in hair!"

Snoopy sat beside Lucy for a while. Then he grew bored, so he ran off to see what Charlie Brown and Sally were up to. Sally was blowing up her beach-ball. Her brother was counting his holiday money. "I'm going to do the most exciting thing of all!" chuckled Charlie Brown, hurrying off towards the beach shop. Snoopy waited to see what it was.

Charlie Brown returned, carrying a beautiful model boat. It was a three-masted sailing ship complete with flags and rigging. "I've saved up all summer for this," he announced, proudly, "and now I'm going to sail it on the sea."

Sally named the ship H.M.S. 'Sweet Babboo' and launched it properly by shaking a few drops of lemonade over the bows. Then everyone clapped and cheered as the model boat bobbed out into the waves. It looked splendid, speeding backwards and forwards on the shimmering sea. Then it disappeared! "I don't know how to tell you this, big brother," exclaimed Sally, "but your ship has sunk!"

Charlie Brown was heartbroken. He wandered along to the other end of the beach and rested his elbows on the sea wall. "It's not fair," he told Sally, who came over to join him, "everything I do goes wrong. I can't play football or baseball; I'm useless at flying my kite; I can't make the Little Red-Haired Girl notice me – and now I can't even sail a model boat!" Sally gave her brother a smile. "I can't beat Martina Navratilova at tennis, but am I worried?" she said.

Meanwhile, just down the beach, Snoopy was thinking about the loss of H.M.S. 'Sweet Babboo'. Suddenly, the beagle had an idea. He hurried to the beach shop where they also hired out diving equipment. "I'll salvage Charlie Brown's boat!" he thought to himself.

Snoopy hired some goggles, flippers and a snorkel. Then he jumped off a jetty into the sea.

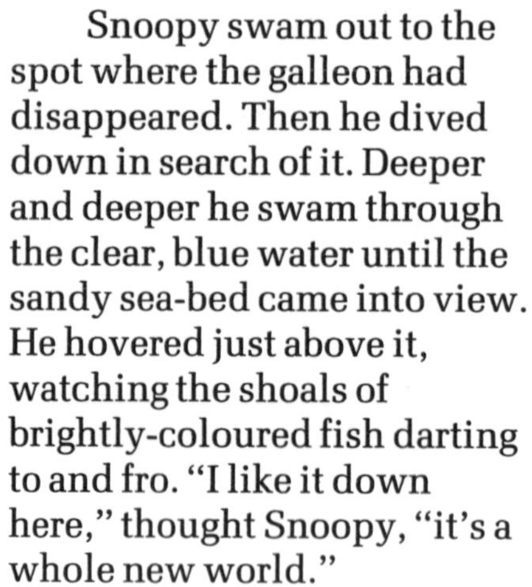

Snoopy swam out to the spot where the galleon had disappeared. Then he dived down in search of it. Deeper and deeper he swam through the clear, blue water until the sandy sea-bed came into view. He hovered just above it, watching the shoals of brightly-coloured fish darting to and fro. "I like it down here," thought Snoopy, "it's a whole new world."

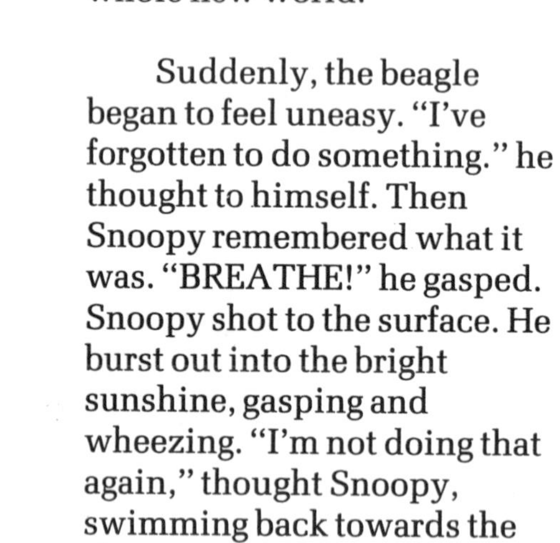

Suddenly, the beagle began to feel uneasy. "I've forgotten to do something." he thought to himself. Then Snoopy remembered what it was. "BREATHE!" he gasped. Snoopy shot to the surface. He burst out into the bright sunshine, gasping and wheezing. "I'm not doing that again," thought Snoopy, swimming back towards the shore, "if I'm going to look for Charlie Brown's sunken galleon, I'm going to do it properly!"

Snoopy returned to the beach shop and traded in his goggles and snorkel for a proper face-mask and oxygen cylinder. "You look like a spaceman!" laughed Linus.

The brave beagle swam out to the wreck-site and dived down again. This time he had plenty of air to breathe and it was not long before he spotted the sunken sailing boat, resting on a sea-weed covered rock. Snoopy raised the boat. "First H.M.S. 'Sweet Babboo'," he murmured through the bubbles, "next a Spanish treasure ship."

Down by the water's edge, Charlie Brown was sitting with a packet of popcorn that he had bought to cheer himself up. He could not believe his eyes when deep-sea diver Snoopy emerged from the waves, carrying his lost boat. "Oh, Snoopy," cried Charlie Brown, leaping to his feet, "you're my best friend in the whole, wide world!"

As a reward, Charlie Brown bought his dog an expensive cooling drink and a slap-up meal from the beach cafe. And he thanked Snoopy over and over again. "Charlie Brown doesn't have to do that," thought Snoopy, the scuba diver, "losing his galleon has made my dreams come true!"